Here's all the great literature in this grade level of *Celebrate Reading!*

TACKY the Penguin

Helen Lester
Illustrated by Lynn Munsinger

HARRY ALLARD

MISS NELSON IS MISSING!

JAMES MARSHALL

The BOY and the GHOST
by Robert D. San Souci / illustrated by J. Brian Pinkney

BOOK A

Pig Tales

Stories That Twist

Miss Nelson Is Missing!
by Harry Allard
Illustrations by James Marshall
✳ CHILDREN'S CHOICE
✳ CALIFORNIA YOUNG READER MEDAL

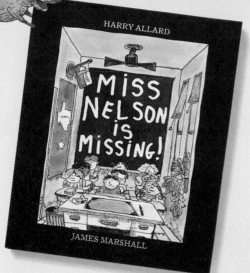

Harvey, the Foolish Pig
retold by Dick Gackenbach

King Wacky
by Dick Gackenbach
✳ CHILDREN'S CHOICE

Featured Poets

Jack Prelutsky
Arnold Lobel

Esmeralda and the Pet Parade
by Cecile Schoberle

**Anansi and the
Moss-Covered Rock**
retold by Eric A. Kimmel
Illustrations by Janet Stevens

Chicken Little
by Steven Kellogg
✳ CHILDREN'S CHOICE

BOOK B

If You Meet a Dragon

and Smaller Challenges

Featured Poets

Alexander Resnikoff

Norma Farber

Frank Asch

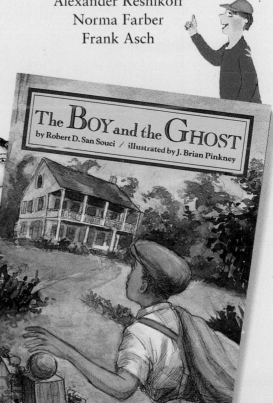

The BOY and the GHOST
by Robert D. San Souci / illustrated by J. Brian Pinkney

BOOK C

How Many Toes Does a Fish Have?

Looking Beneath the Surface

Featured Poet

Joan W. Blos

BOOK E

Dinner with Aliens

and Other Unexpected Situations

Featured Poet

Lucille Clifton

BOOK F

In Your Wildest Dreams

Imagination at Work

Featured Poets

A. A. Milne
Bill Peet

Celebrate Reading!
Trade Book Library

The Cactus Flower Bakery
by Harry Allard
✳ CHILDREN'S CHOICE AUTHOR

Play Ball, Amelia Bedelia
by Peggy Parish

Fables
by Arnold Lobel
✳ CALDECOTT MEDAL
✳ ALA NOTABLE BOOK

What's Cooking, Jenny Archer?
by Ellen Conford
✳ PARENTS' CHOICE AUTHOR

**She Come Bringing Me
That Little Baby Girl**
by Eloise Greenfield
✳ IRMA SIMONTON BLACK AWARD
✳ BOSTON GLOBE-HORN BOOK
ILLUSTRATION HONOR
✳ CHILDREN'S CHOICE

The Show-and-Tell War
by Janice Lee Smith
✳ CHILDREN'S CHOICE
✳ *SCHOOL LIBRARY JOURNAL* BEST BOOK

King of the Birds
by Shirley Climo
✳ NOTABLE SOCIAL STUDIES TRADE BOOK

Fossils Tell of Long Ago
by Aliki
✳ LIBRARY OF CONGRESS
CHILDREN'S BOOK
✳ OUTSTANDING SCIENCE TRADE BOOK

Willie's Not the Hugging Kind
by Joyce Durham Barrett

The Paper Crane
by Molly Bang
✳ ALA NOTABLE CHILDREN'S BOOK
✳ BOSTON GLOBE-HORN BOOK AWARD
✳ *SCHOOL LIBRARY JOURNAL* BEST BOOK
✳ READING RAINBOW SELECTION

Don't Tell the Whole World
by Joanna Cole
✳ CHILDREN'S CHOICE AUTHOR

**The Spooky Tail of
Prewitt Peacock**
by Bill Peet
✳ CHILDREN'S CHOICE AUTHOR

Pig Tales

STORIES THAT TWIST

Titles in This Set

Cover Artist
Henrik Drescher lives with his wife
and two kids in the mountains of
upstate New York, where he makes
children's books, eats apples,
yodels, and hikes.

ISBN 0-673-81139-5

1997
Scott, Foresman and Company, Glenview, Illinois
All Rights Reserved.
Printed in the United States of America.

Acknowledgments appear on page 144.

345678910DQ0100999897

Pig Tales

STORIES THAT TWIST

ScottForesman

Contents

It's Right Before Your Eyes!

Animal Tails
Genre Study

Expect the Unexpected with Dick Gackenbach

Author Study

Student Resources

The kids in Room 207 were misbehaving again.
Spitballs stuck to the ceiling.
Paper planes whizzed through the air.
They were the worst-behaved class in the whole school.

"Now settle down," said Miss Nelson in a sweet voice.
But the class would *not* settle down.

They whispered and giggled.
They squirmed and made faces.

They were even rude during story hour.
And they always refused to do their lessons.
"Something will have to be done," said Miss Nelson.

The next morning Miss Nelson did not come to school. "Wow!" yelled the kids. "Now we can *really* act up!"
They began to make more spitballs and paper planes. "Today let's be just terrible!" they said.

"Not so fast!" hissed an unpleasant voice.

A woman in an ugly black dress stood before them.
"I am your new teacher, Miss Viola Swamp."
And she rapped the desk with her ruler.
"Where is Miss Nelson?" asked the kids.

"Never mind that!" snapped Miss Swamp. "Open those
arithmetic books!"

Miss Nelson's kids did as they were told.

They could see that Miss Swamp was a real witch.

She meant business.

Right away she put them to work.

And she loaded them down with homework.

"We'll have no story hour today," said Miss Swamp.

"Keep your mouths shut," said Miss Swamp.

"Sit perfectly still," said Miss Swamp.

"And if you misbehave, you'll be sorry," said Miss Swamp.

The kids in Room 207 had *never* worked so hard.
Days went by and there was no sign of Miss Nelson.
The kids *missed* Miss Nelson!
"Maybe we should try to find her," they said.
Some of them went to the police.
Detective McSmogg was assigned to the case.
He listened to their story.
He scratched his chin.
"Hmmmm," he said. "Hmmm."
"I think Miss Nelson is missing."
Detective McSmogg would
not be much help.

Other kids went to Miss Nelson's house.
The shades were tightly drawn, and no one answered
the door. In fact, the only person they *did* see was the wicked
Miss Viola Swamp, coming up the street.
"If she sees us, she'll give us more homework."
They got away just in time.

Maybe something *terrible* happened to ~~Miss Nelson~~! Mr. Nelson

"Maybe she was gobbled up by a shark!" said one of the kids.

But that didn't seem likely.

"Maybe ~~Miss Nelson~~ went to Mars!" said another kid. Mr. Nelson

But that didn't seem likely either.

"I know!" exclaimed one know-it-all. "Maybe ~~Miss Nelson's~~ Mr. Nelson's

car was carried off by a swarm of angry butterflies!"

But that was the least likely of all.

The kids in Room 207 became very discouraged.

It seemed that ~~Miss Nelson~~ was never coming back. Mr. Nelson

And they would be stuck with Miss Viola Swamp forever.

They heard footsteps in the hall.

"Here comes the witch," they whispered.

"Hello, children," someone said in a sweet voice.

17

It was Miss Nelson!

"Did you miss me?" she asked.

"We certainly did!" cried all the kids.

"Where were you?"

"That's my little secret," said Miss Nelson.

"How about a story hour?"

"Oh, yes!" cried the kids.

Miss Nelson noticed that during story hour no one
was rude or silly.

"What brought about this lovely change?" she asked.

"That's *our* little secret," said the kids.

Back home Miss Nelson took off her coat and hung it
in the closet (right next to an ugly black dress).
When it was time for bed she sang a little song.
"I'll never tell," she said to herself with a smile.

P.S. Detective McSmogg is working on a new case.
He is *now* looking for Miss Viola Swamp.

THINKING ABOUT IT

1. How would you have felt when Miss Nelson returned? What would you have done to show her?

2. Detective McSmogg couldn't find Miss Nelson. Can you? What are the clues in the story and in the pictures that will help you find her? How will they help you?

3. Viola Swamp may return! To keep this from happening, make a list of rules the class should try to follow.

Three Cheers for Miss Nelson

The football team needs someone to whip them into shape, and Miss Nelson knows just the person in *Miss Nelson Has a Field Day* by Harry Allard.

ESMERALDA

AND THE PET PARADE

CECILE SCHOBERLE

rom the
beginning, Esmeralda was
always in trouble.

If the flowers were
eaten, a trash can knocked
over, or Mama's clean
laundry pulled down from
the line, everyone knew
who had done it.

"Esmeraaalda!" Mama would scream. "Juan, come and get that goat of yours!"

"Golly, Essie," Juan would whisper. "Can't you be good?"

On Sunday, Juan's Aunt Bertha came to tea. And on Sunday, Esmeralda decided she liked to roll on the living room rug better than in her bath towel.

On Friday, Juan tried to teach Esmeralda to fetch Papa's slippers. And on Saturday, Mr. Kent, who lived five blocks away, brought them back.

Everyone in the family was against that goat. All except Grandpa. He called her his little explorer. "Columbus, Cortez, Cabeza de Vaca," he said. "The way that goat roams—I tell you, someday she will be famous!"

randpa had brought her over from his ranch one morning, all bundled up. When Juan saw that fuzzy white face and those mischievous eyes, he knew he'd found a friend.

That was a year ago. A year full of trouble. But a year full of friendship. When Juan came home from school, Esmeralda was the first to greet him. They did homework together, waded in the creek together, even flew kites together. And if Juan ever needed a friend just to listen, Essie was there.

"Esmeralda," Juan said as he brushed her, "when are you going to grow up and behave? I want Mama and Papa to be as proud of you as I am."

She just smiled and nuzzled his hand. Then she ate the ribbon he'd tied to her horn.

t the neighborhood playground there was magic in the air. It was the week of the Fiesta, the time when the whole city came together to celebrate—with pageants, dancing, and singing. Best of all was the Pet Parade. The children of Santa Fe marched through town with their pets dressed in wild and wonderful costumes. There would be bands playing, crowds cheering, and special prizes for the best-dressed. It was hard to think about anything else.

Juan aimed the ball, then stopped. "How about if I dress Esmeralda as Cinderella? Really show her off."

Lucy grabbed the ball and shot. "Point! Gee, I'm not so sure. I just want one of us on Garcia Street to win first prize."

"Me too," yelled Roberto from his bike. "And Juan. . . ." He looked over at Esmeralda. "Make sure that goat stays in line."

Next day, the gang met in Roberto's backyard. "Any ideas for our costumes?" asked Roberto.

arlotta waved brightly colored flags. "We could go as different countries."

"Neat idea!" said Myron. "Who goes as which country?"

"I want to be the U.S.A. And nobody else can," said Roberto.

"Oh, forget it, Roberto," huffed Carlotta.

"How about if we dress our pets as dinosaurs?" said Myron.

"Cool!" exclaimed Lucy. Then she giggled and held up Hamlet, her hamster. "But what kind of monster could this little guy be?" They all rolled with laughter.

"Why don't we choose our own costumes, but all go in the same color?" suggested Carlotta.

"Hmm—you mean, like all dress in blue?" asked Roberto.

"You could put blue paper streamers on your bike, like the floats at the football parade," said Juan excitedly.

"I could decorate my dad's blue fishing hat!" said Myron.

o it was settled. Juan and Myron made plans as they walked home. But as they parted, Myron's last words were, "Juan, don't let your Esmeralda ruin our chances."

Juan was quiet as he and Papa drove over to Grandpa's that evening.

"Something bothering you?" asked Papa. Usually Juan would be excited about a visit to the ranch.

"No, sir," said Juan.

Grandpa greeted Juan at the front door with a hug. "Why this sad face, boy? Come, let's go watch my sunset."

When the evening colors changed day into night, Grandpa could always be found on his back porch. From there, he could watch the stars coming out, and feel the cooling breeze from the distant mountain. It really was Grandpa's sunset, because it was like no other place in the world.

"Grandpa," said Juan slowly, "nobody believes in Esmeralda. They think she wanders, gets into trouble, can't behave. And Grandpa . . . nobody believes in me."

Watching a lone hawk circle, Grandpa turned to sit by Juan.

"You can't change some things, Juanito. Let her be as she is. And remember what I have always told you about your little explorer."

Juan grinned. Grandpa began, "Columbus, Cortez, Cabeza de Vaca. The way that goat roams, I tell you . . . ."

". . . someday she will be famous!" Juan chimed in. They laughed and Juan gave Grandpa a big hug.

"Finally! A smile! Now let me show you my newest creation." From pieces of cottonwood and cedar, Grandpa carved beautiful animals and santos. Into Juan's hands he placed a tiny wooden bird.

racias!" called Juan again and again, as Papa backed the truck out of the driveway.

"Remember, Juan," called Grandpa. "It would be easier to change the wild bird in the sky than to change your Esmeralda."

On the day of the Parade Juan awoke with Essie nibbling on his pajama leg. He scrambled into his special blue vest and Fiesta tie, then carefully tied Mama's new blue chiffon scarf around Esmeralda's neck.

"Here's a costume so simple that even you can't mess it up, Esmeralda." He patted her freshly washed head and gave her horns a final polish. Esmeralda smiled up at him.

"I know you'll do your best today, Essie. But, just in case. . . ." Juan reached into a drawer, took out a leash, and clicked it around her neck.

A dog leash! Esmeralda had never worn one before. She balked and pulled. "Come on, Essie," said Juan. "It's for your own good."

Juan managed to get Esmeralda to the Parade, but she wasn't happy.

Hundreds of people had gathered. There were costumes in all colors, and pets of all shapes and sizes.

"Ladies and gentlemen," the announcer called, "time to begin. Keep the dogs away from the cats, and the cats away from the dogs. And remember—don't

get behind a horse. Good luck, and have fun!"

The Garcia gang moved forward. Juan pulled Esmeralda along. She shook her head, trying to get rid of the strange leash. "Easy, Essie," Juan ordered. At the corner, he saw Grandpa and waved.

Suddenly, a car backfired. Esmeralda jumped with fright, snapping the leash.

top!" screamed Juan. "Look out! Runaway goat!"

Through the plaza Esmeralda ran. Past the Fiesta dancers, past the snack stand selling Navajo fry bread, past a very surprised policeman.

Esmeralda ran down the alley, knocking over trash cans, scattering newspapers and boxes.

Shaking and snorting, she couldn't rid herself of that leash. Leaping over a rosebush, she landed in a backyard. Straight on she ran, right through the clothesline and around the corner.

"Esmeralda!" screamed Juan, panting and running behind. "Alto! Stop!"

Esmeralda could hear Juan's voice from far down the block. She hopped over a bicycle stand. A car roared toward her and she bounded over the curb. Gathering speed, she also gathered everything in her path—signs, sunglasses, sheets—as she ran up and back through the Parade.

top, Esmeralda, stop!" yelled the children of the Garcia Street neighborhood. Esmeralda skidded into the churchyard. Wham! She knocked over a rummage sale table, sending feathered hats and old handbags flying.

Now she really was trying to stop, but it was too late. Esmeralda, the goat who liked to roam, slid to a halt—right in front of the judges' stand.

Juan and Grandpa both ran up. "Ooh, Essie!" groaned Juan when he saw her. It was a sight wild enough to make him cry. The judge rose slowly and peered over the stand.

"Is this your goat, young man?"

Juan looked over at the Garcia Street gang as they stared in horror. Behind them, Mama and Papa frowned. Juan looked up at the very tall judge. "Yes, sir. This is my Esmeralda."

Esmeralda gazed up at Juan and smiled. Then she nuzzled his hand.

The judge raised the microphone. "For the Most Unusual Costume—the winner is Esmeralda, the goat of Garcia Street!"

The crowd clapped as the giant blue ribbon was hung on Esmeralda. The Garcia gang couldn't stop cheering for their winner. And Juan's face beamed as Grandpa gave him a big wink.

Because they both knew . . . that someday that goat would be famous.

Thinking About It

1. You are visiting Santa Fe, New Mexico, and you've just seen the Pet Parade. What will you tell a friend or family member about the parade and the first-place winner, Esmeralda?

2. What did Juan's friends think about Esmeralda before the parade? How do you think they will feel about Esmeralda now that she's won first place? What makes you think so?

3. Choose a pet that you would like to have in a pet parade. How would you prepare your pet for the parade? Why?

Anything for a Pet
Annabel wants a pet of her own, but her dad is allergic to every pet Annabel can think of in *Snakes Are Nothing to Sneeze At* by Gabrielle Charbonnet.

A Goat Wandered Into a Junkyard

by Jack Prelutsky

A goat wandered into a junkyard

in search of an afternoon meal,

he started with remnants of rubber

and several fragments of steel.

He nibbled a couple of axles,

he gobbled up gauges and gears,

he gnawed on a tangle of wires

and colorful plastic veneers.

He polished off various bearings,

he munched on a mountain of brass,

he bolted a heap of upholstery

and numerous panels of glass.

He put away pistons and pedals,

then followed a fender or two

with most of a standard transmission,

and they aren't easy to chew.

He ate an assortment of sprockets,

he swallowed some springs by the coil,

then washed down his lunch with a gallon

of forty-weight premium oil.

As soon as that goat had digested

his odd but industrious meal,

he coughed and he coughed

and he coughed and he coughed

and he coughed up an automobile.

Anansi and the Moss-Covered Rock

retold by Eric A. Kimmel
illustrations by Janet Stevens

Once upon a time Anansi the Spider was walking, walking, walking through the forest when something caught his eye. It was a strange moss-covered rock.

"How interesting!" Anansi said. "Isn't this a strange moss-covered rock!"

KPOM! Everything went black. Down fell Anansi, senseless.

An hour later Anansi woke up. His head was spinning. He wondered what had happened.

"I was walking along the path when something caught my eye. I stopped and said, 'Isn't this a strange moss-covered rock.' "

KPOM! Down fell Anansi again. But this time, when he woke up an hour later, he knew what was happening.

"Aha!" said Anansi. "This is a magic rock. And whenever anyone comes along and says the magic words, 'Isn't this a strange hmm-hmmmmm hmm,' down he goes. This is a good thing to know," said Anansi. "And I know just how to use it."

So Anansi went walking, walking, walking through the forest until he came to Lion's house. Lion was sitting on his porch. At his feet was a great pile of yams. Anansi loved yams, but he was too lazy to dig them up himself. Anansi said to Lion, "Hello, Lion! It is very hot today. Don't you think so?"

"Yes, Anansi," said Lion. "It is terribly hot."

"I am going for a walk in the cool jungle," said Anansi. "Would you like to come?"

"I certainly would," said Lion.

So Lion and Anansi went walking, walking, walking through the forest. After a while Anansi led Lion to a certain place.

"Lion! Do you see what I see?"

"Oh, yes, Anansi!" said Lion. "Isn't this a strange moss-covered rock!"

KPOM! Down fell Lion. Anansi ran back to Lion's house and made off with Lion's yams.

An hour later Lion woke up. His head was
spinning. Anansi was nowhere in sight. And when
he got home, he found that every single one of his
yams was gone. Lion was very sad.

But Anansi was very happy. He couldn't wait to play his trick again.

Once more Anansi went walking, walking, walking through the forest. This time he stopped at Elephant's house. Elephant was sitting on his porch. At Elephant's feet was a great pile of bananas. Anansi loved bananas, but he was too lazy to pick them himself. So he said to Elephant, "Hello, Elephant! Isn't it hot today!"

"It is!" Elephant agreed.

"I am going for a walk in the cool forest," Anansi said. "Would you like to come?"

"That sounds nice," said Elephant. "Thank you for inviting me, Anansi."

So Anansi and Elephant went walking, walking, walking through the forest. After a while Anansi led Elephant to a certain place.

"Elephant! Look! Do you see what I see?"

Elephant looked. "Yes, I do, Anansi. Isn't this a strange moss-covered rock!"

KPOM! Down fell Elephant. Anansi ran back to Elephant's house and made off with all the bananas.

An hour later Elephant woke up. His head was spinning. Anansi was nowhere in sight. And when he got home, he found that every single one of his bananas was gone. Elephant was very sad.

But Anansi was very happy. He couldn't wait
to play his trick again. He played it on Rhinoceros

and Hippopotamus.

He played it on Giraffe

and Zebra. He played it on every single animal
in the forest.

But all this time, watching from behind the leaves, was Little Bush Deer. Little Bush Deer is small and shy, and very hard to see. She watched Anansi play his wicked trick again and again on all the other animals. Little Bush Deer decided it was time for Anansi to learn a lesson.

So Little Bush Deer went deep into the forest to where the coconut trees grow. She climbed a coconut tree and threw down a great many coconuts. She carried the coconuts home in a basket and set them on her porch. Then she sat down beside them to wait.

In a little while along came Anansi. Anansi's eyes lit up when he saw Little Bush Deer's coconuts. Anansi loved coconuts. He loved to eat the tender white coconut meat and drink the sweet coconut milk inside. But he was much too lazy to gather coconuts himself.

Instead he said, "Hello, Little Bush Deer! It is so hot today!"

Little Bush Deer smiled. "It is very hot, Anansi."

"I am going for a walk in the cool forest. Would you like to come?"

"Yes, I would," said Little Bush Deer.

So Anansi and Little Bush Deer went walking, walking, walking in the cool forest. After a while Anansi led Little Bush Deer to a certain place.

"Little Bush Deer! Look over there! Do you see what I see?"

Little Bush Deer knew all about Anansi's trick. She looked. "No, Anansi. I don't see anything."

"You must see it. Look very carefully."

Little Bush Deer looked. "No. I still don't see anything," she said.

Anansi began to get angry. "You must see it. Look over here. Look right where I'm pointing. Do you see it now?"

"No, Anansi," said Little Bush Deer.

Anansi stamped his legs. "You see it. You just don't want to say it."

"Say what?" said Little Bush Deer.

"You know."

"Is that what I'm supposed to say?"

"Yes," said Anansi.

"All right. Then I will say it to make you happy. 'You know,' " said Little Bush Deer. "There! I said it. Are you satisfied?"

"No!" Anansi shouted. "You're not supposed to say 'You know!' "

"What am I supposed to say?"

"You're supposed to say, 'Isn't this a strange moss-covered rock!' "

KPOM! Down fell Anansi.

Little Bush Deer ran and got all the other animals.
Together they went to Anansi's house and took back all
the good things he had stolen from them.

An hour later Anansi woke up. His head was spinning. Little Bush Deer was nowhere in sight. And when he got home, he found his house as empty as it was before.

But if you think Anansi learned his lesson, you're mistaken.

Because he's still playing tricks to this very day.

Thinking About It

1 Disappearing yams and bananas! What next? You are one of the animals in the story. Which animal are you? What favorite food of yours does Anansi try to steal? What do you do to stop him?

2 Little Bush Deer thinks Anansi should be taught a lesson. What is it? Do you agree? Why?

3 Anansi used the moss-covered rock to trick the other animals. What else could you do with the moss-covered rock? Would your idea be helpful or harmful to others?

Tricked Again!
Shorty Long owes Widow Macrae some money. This trickster thinks he has found a sure way to outfox the widow in *Four Dollars and Fifty Cents* by Eric A. Kimmel.

FOUR DOLLARS AND FIFTY CENTS

by Eric A. Kimmel
illustrated by Glen Rounds

Chicken Little

Retold and illustrated by Steven Kellogg

oultry coming," announced Foxy Loxy, as he spotted Chicken Little skipping down the road.

"That little featherhead will make a tasty chicken-salad sandwich," he chuckled.

But before Chicken Little got close enough for Foxy Loxy to pounce, an acorn fell from an oak tree and hit her on the head.

"Help! Help! The sky is falling!" shrieked the little bird.

Her cries were heard by Henny Penny.
"What's the matter?" she asked.

"The sky is falling!" cried Chicken Little. "A piece
of it hit me on the head."

Henny Penny was horrified.

"Call the police!" she cried. "The sky is falling!
The sky is falling!"

"That hen has a plump pair of drumsticks," observed
Foxy Loxy, "and they'll be mighty tasty southern-fried."
He was about to charge forward and capture the two
chickens when the clamor reached Ducky Lucky.

"What's all this cackling about?" he demanded.

"The sky is falling!" cried Henny Penny. "A piece of it hit Chicken Little on the head."

"This is terrible!" squawked Ducky Lucky. And together the three birds wailed: "Help! Police! The sky is falling!"

Foxy Loxy shivered with greed when he imagined how delicious Ducky Lucky would taste simmered in spices and sauce.

But before he could spring from his hiding place, the cries
of the group were heard by Goosey Lucy and Gosling Gilbert.

"What luck!" whispered the fox. "I'll toast the bite-sized one as soon as I get home, and I'll pop the fat one into the freezer until Christmas."

Foxy Loxy almost fainted with delight when Turkey Lurkey came running across the fields. "There's my Thanksgiving feast!" he chuckled. "This is the luckiest day of my life."

He was about to pounce on his victims when suddenly he realized it was six against one. "And that turkey and goose look like pretty tough birds," he murmured.

"I'll avoid a scuffle by outsmarting those foolish fowl."
Disguising his truck and himself, he approached the group and announced: "Officer Loxy at your service, folks. What seems to be the problem?"

"The sky is falling!" chorused the birds.

"A piece of it hit me on the head!" added Chicken Little.

"This *is* an emergency!" declared the fox. "Into the truck, and I'll take you directly to headquarters!"

Suddenly, as she looked more closely at the fox, Chicken Little remembered the wanted poster she had seen in town.

"It's Foxy Loxy!" she shrieked. "Run for your lives!" The birds tried to escape, but Foxy Loxy threw Chicken Little into the truck and locked the door.

Before driving off, the fox couldn't resist reading the recipes he had selected for each of his captives.

"And as for that nonsense about the sky falling," he sneered, "this is what beaned the dim-witted chick!"

With a triumphant laugh he hurled the acorn skyward, jumped into the truck, and cried, "On to the kitchen!"

The acorn soared above the treetops and lodged itself
in the propeller gears of a sky patrol helicopter piloted
by Sergeant Hippo Hefty.

The gears jammed, the propeller stopped turning, and the helicopter plunged toward the earth.

The falling helicopter crashed into the cab of the poultry truck. Foxy Loxy leaped from the wreckage screaming, "THE SKY IS FALLING! THE SKY IS FALLING!"

"Stop that thug!" cried the birds.
  Sergeant Hefty flattened the fleeing fox.

"You're under arrest!" he announced.
  "You mean I'm under a fat hippo," snapped Foxy Loxy.

During his trial, Foxy Loxy insisted that he was innocent. But the judge sent him to prison on a diet of green-bean gruel and weed juice.

On her way home, Chicken Little recovered the acorn. She planted it next to her coop.

Years later, when the acorn had grown into an oak tree, her grandchildren loved to snuggle beside Chicken Little and listen to her adventure.

Thinking About It

 You're one of the animals that Chicken Little meets after the acorn has beaned her on the head. How will you convince her that it's not the sky that's falling at all?

 In this animal fantasy the animals can talk. What else can they do that real animals usually cannot do?

 What if *Chicken Little* were a movie? What kind of an advertisement could you make up for it? What scene would you use in the ad to make people want to see the movie? Explain why yours is a good choice.

Harvey,
the Foolish Pig

RETOLD AND ILLUSTRATED BY DICK GACKENBACH

Once there was a pig named Harvey. Harvey was an ordinary pig except that he was poorer than most. His trousers were covered in patches and he had no shoes.

Harvey hated being poor and wanted to be rich. So one day he decided to go in search of the wise and great King of Animals.

"I will ask the King a question," Harvey told himself. "I will ask him how I, Harvey Pig, can become rich."

That very day Harvey set off to find the King.

Soon after Harvey began his journey, he met a hungry wolf.

"Where are you going?" the wolf asked the pig.

"To find the wise King of Animals," replied Harvey. "I have a question to ask him!"

"Well," said the wolf, "when you find him, ask him a question for me, too. Tell the King you met a hungry wolf who doesn't have a thing to eat. Ask him if he knows where I can find a good meal."

Harvey nodded. "I will," he promised. And then he went on his way.

A little farther along, Harvey met a pretty pig named Louella.

"Sit and stay a while," Louella invited Harvey.

"I'm in a hurry," he answered. "I must find the wise King of Animals. I have a question to ask him."

"Go then," said Louella, "but when you find the King ask him a question for me as well. Tell him I am very pretty and very rich, but I am very unhappy. Ask him what will make me happy."

Harvey promised Louella he would ask the King, and then he continued his journey.

Next Harvey met a thirsty tree. Even though it was summer, the tree's leaves were parched and brown.

"Where are you going in such a rush?" the tree asked the pig.

"To find the wise King of Animals," said Harvey. "I have a question to ask him."

"Ah," said the tree. "And when you find him will you ask a question for a poor tree, too?"

"All right," said Harvey. He hoped he could keep all the questions straight.

"Then tell the King you met a tree that lives by the side of a river, yet is always dry and thirsty. Ask him if my leaves will ever turn green again."

Harvey gave the tree his promise and then rushed on, for he was anxious to find the King.

At last, after passing over meadows bright with sunshine and forests deep in shadows, Harvey found the wise King.

The little pig knelt before His Majesty and waited for him to speak.

"Greetings, Pig!" said the Protector of All Creatures. "The birds have told me of your journey. Why do you seek me out?"

"Well," said Harvey, "the world is full of riches while I have patches on my trousers and can afford no shoes."

"That is so," remarked the King.

"Then, sir," pleaded Harvey, "may I not have some riches, too?"

"I will give you the Gift of Good Luck," replied the King. "If you deserve them, you may have all the riches you will ever need. But," he warned, "you must find them first."

"Where will I look for them?" asked Harvey.

"Keep your eyes and ears open, and use your head," said the King. "They will show you the way. Now be off with you."

Before Harvey departed to find his riches, he remembered his promise and asked the King the questions for the hungry wolf, the beautiful Louella, and the dry tree.

The King listened patiently while scratching his mane. Then he gave Harvey three wise answers to take back with him.

Harvey thanked the King and hurried off to search for his riches.

The thirsty tree was happy to see the pig return.

"What answer did the King send me?" the tree asked Harvey.

"He told me to tell you there is a pot of gold buried beneath your roots," explained Harvey. "Until it is removed, no water will ever reach your leaves and you will not bear fruit again."

The tree's limbs began to shake.

"What are you waiting for?" he shouted. "Remove the gold, you foolish pig."

"No, no," said Harvey. "I have no time. I must go and find my riches."

And off he ran.

Louella Pig was eagerly awaiting Harvey's return, too.

"Does the King have an answer for me?" she asked.

"Yes," replied Harvey. "He told me to tell you that you are unhappy because you are lonely. He said you should find someone to share your life with you. Only then will you be happy."

"Marry me then," Louella pleaded, "and we will both be happy."

"I'm sorry, but I can't right now," said Harvey as he ran away. "I must find my riches!"

"Oh, you foolish pig," said Louella sadly.

Farther down the road, Harvey met the hungry wolf again.

"What does the King have to say to me?" asked the wolf. "Did he send me a good meal?"

"Oh, so much has happened," said Harvey, sitting down to catch his breath. "On my way to see the King, I met Louella Pig who was so unhappy despite her wealth and beauty. Then I met a thirsty tree who wanted to know how to get some water.

"Well," continued Harvey, "the King told me to tell the tree to remove a pot of gold from beneath its roots, and he told me to tell Louella to get herself a husband. Then and only then would Louella be happy and the tree would get water. WHEW!"

"And did you tell them?" asked the wolf.

"I did indeed!" replied Harvey. "And Louella wanted me to marry her, and the tree wanted me to remove the gold."

"What did you do?" asked the wolf.

"I had to refuse, of course," said Harvey. "The King gave me the Gift of Good Luck and I am in a hurry to find my riches."

"Well, before you go," said the wolf, "what did the King have to say to me?"

"Oh, yes," said Harvey. "I almost forgot. The King told me to tell you that you may meet a foolish pig with patches on his trousers and no shoes who doesn't know his good luck when he sees it."

"Then what?" asked the wolf eagerly. "Then what does the King say I should do?"

"Eat him!" said Harvey.

THE END

Thinking About It

1. You are going along with Harvey on his trip to see the King of the Animals. What advice do you give him?

2. You be the judge! Harvey and the wolf disagree, and it's up to you to settle the question. Should Harvey be eaten by the wolf? Tell your reasons.

3. At the last minute Harvey makes a daring escape. How can he get away from the wolf? What will happen next?

More Illustrations by Dick Gackenbach

There are lots of changes in store for Adam Joshua in *Baby Blues* by Janice Lee Smith.

KING WACKY

DICK GACKENBACH

In the tiny kingdom of Woosey, a baby was born. It was a boy—the son of the king, and a most unusual baby.

"Isn't he beautiful?" said his mother, the queen.

"He is, my dear," replied the king. "But, dear lady, his head is on backward!"

"So it is, dear sir," said the queen. "But, no matter, we will love our son all the more for that."

The good people who lived in Woosey thought the same. "He is our prince," they said, "and we will love him too, no matter which way his head is on."

When Prince Wacky, as the boy was finally named, was old enough to walk, he walked backward.

When the prince began to talk, he spoke in a backward manner as well. Wacky said "goodbye" when he was coming. He said "hello" when he was going. It was "good night" in the morning and "good morning" at night.

In the beginning all this was confusing, but in time it was expected that whatever the prince did, he would do backward. He brushed his teeth before he ate and washed his hands after each meal. When Prince Wacky dined, he sat on the table and his food was placed on a chair.

Over the years, as Prince Wacky grew to be a man, the people of Woosey became truly fond of their backward prince.

"He is kind," they said of him. "Our dear prince has a good heart and is always fair."

So when the day came that Prince Wacky replaced the old king, the people cheered from the bottom of their hearts.

"LONG LIVE KING WACKY," they shouted.

And then, just to please their new king, the people cheered him backward. "WACKY KING LIVE LONG," they cried happily.

Young King Wacky's backward ways made him the most popular king the land of Woosey ever had.

"From now on," King Wacky ordered, "the king will pay taxes to the people." This law made everybody in Woosey very rich.

"Let all the clocks run backward," King Wacky decreed. Because of this law, no one ever complained of being late again.

"Serve the dessert first," King Wacky commanded all the cooks in the land. "And bring the Brussels sprouts last!" From then on, everyone who lived in Woosey always had room in his belly for a good piece of pie. With Wacky as king everyone agreed it was a joy to live in the land of Woosey.

One day the noble lords of King Wacky's court advised their king: "It is time," they let him know, "for you to have a queen."

"Ah," King Wacky nodded. "That is a bad idea."

The king's reply pleased his noble lords; they knew their king well! When King Wacky said "out," he meant "in." *Up* meant *down; down* meant *up. Good* meant *bad,* and *bad* meant *good.* Therefore, the lords knew King Wacky was willing to seek a queen.

With the king's permission, the lords wrote a message to be sent to mighty King Tub in the nearby land of Bumble.

"In the name of our gracious King Wacky," the message said, "we request the hand of your daughter, Princess Honey, in marriage."

"Perhaps," one lord suggested, "we should add a word or two about King Wacky's unusual ways."

"No, no!" insisted the other lords. "That would never do."

And so, the letter was sealed with the royal seal.

"You will wait for an answer," the lords told the messenger.

Days passed. Finally a tired messenger returned with King Tub's answer. "A splendid idea," King Tub replied. "A marriage would unite Bumble and Woosey. My daughter will arrive to meet your king in seven days."

"Wonderful news!" said the noble lords, "but only seven days to make ready!"

Plans began immediately for the arrival of the future queen.

Bakers baked all sorts and sizes of wedding cakes. Tailors sewed lavish clothes from dawn to sunset. Flags were hung, streets were washed, and houses freshly painted. Schools were closed and peddlers came from everywhere. Woosey was like a giant carnival.

Then, on the seventh day, as promised, Princess Honey arrived at the palace door in her royal carriage. Crowds cheered and danced in the streets as the lovely princess was taken to meet the king.

King Wacky fell in love with the princess the moment he saw her. She was the most beautiful lady King Wacky had ever seen.

Unfortunately, he chose that moment to tell her so.

"Honey," King Wacky said tenderly, "you are the ugliest thing I've ever seen!"

Hearing this, the poor princess burst into a flood of tears. She ran from the palace, home to her father in the land of Bumble.

"King Wacky said I was ugly," Honey sobbed to her
father.

Proud King Tub was furious when he heard how King
Wacky had ill-treated his dear daughter. In a fit of
temper, he made a vow. "I'll have King Wacky's head on
a stick," he said.

"Call my generals," King Tub shouted. "March the
army to the gates of Woosey," he commanded. "Declare
war! Show mercy to no one!"

News of King Tub's marching army traveled fast. Rumors of the coming war spread throughout the land of Woosey.

"It will be a terrible war," everyone agreed. "King Tub's army is a mighty force." The women and children wept and wondered what would become of them. The men of Woosey were sad and thoughtful.

"Perhaps King Wacky will find a way to keep the peace," the people hoped. Everyone gathered at the palace and waited for word from their good king.

Inside the palace, King Wacky and his noble lords were as upset as the people. No one knew what to do. No one wanted war.

"We must tell King Tub that King Wacky meant no harm," suggested a noble lord. "He must understand that when our king says ugly, he means beautiful."

"There is no time for that," said another lord. "King Tub's army is at our very gates."

"Then we must fight," all the lords agreed, "or we will be thought cowards."

So, war it was, and war it would have to be.

"You," King Wacky was told, "will have to tell the people so."

Sadly, King Wacky went out on his balcony and faced the crowd. His subjects were silent and waited anxiously to hear what he had to say.

"I HAVE GOOD NEWS," King Wacky shouted. "WE ARE AT PEACE!"

The people heard no more. Their hearts filled with joy; their cheers reached to heaven. In their great desire for peace, the people had forgotten their king's backward ways. They had forgotten that *good* meant *bad* and that *peace* meant *war.* Had they remembered, they would have hurried home for their weapons and prepared for a cruel war.

Instead, the happy people of Woosey opened their gates and ran to greet King Tub's waiting army. The people kissed the soldiers of Bumble and showered them with gifts and flowers.

King Tub's generals were surprised and confused.

"What do you think has happened?" asked one general.

"Wacky and Tub must have made up," said another.

The generals and the soldiers returned the kisses to the people of Woosey, tossed away their weapons, and went back home to their families in Bumble.

Now there was time enough to explain everything to King Tub. Once he and Princess Honey understood King Wacky's backward ways, all was forgiven and forgotten.

In due time, there was a grand royal wedding.

"Do you take Princess Honey to be your loving wife?"
King Wacky was asked.

"I do not," he answered. But everyone knew he meant
he did.

"WACKY KING LIVE LONG!" the people cheered.

CONVERSATIONS WITH MY DOG

BY DICK GACKENBACH

I have always lived with dachshunds. The current dachshund eating me out of house and home is a ten-year-old named Poppy, and already an authority on everything. The dear dog has a ready wit and can hold her own in any conversation, although there are times when her opinions are quite silly.

"Children don't read much anymore," is her latest silly remark. "They watch TV instead," she insisted.

"Nonsense!" I replied. "When you watch TV you watch the same thing with 30 million other people. When you read a book, you are on your own, and that makes you

128

something special. Kids know that. That is why they always find time to read.

Poppy didn't answer. She never admits when she is wrong.

Very often I read Poppy a new story that I have written. It is an activity she is very fond of, for it gives her a chance to go out of her way to point out an error. "You missed a comma. That should be capitalized!" she is fond of saying. But there are times, with the hope of getting a cookie, she'll toss me a compliment like, "Just where do you get all those great ideas?"

"Good question, Poppy," I said, "for ideas are the keys to good stories. I get my ideas from experiences in my life, and that includes my feelings and emotions. They inspire stories, too. Many of my books are about things that made me happy, things that made me sad, even things that made me mad."

"Did you write a book about me chewing the rug?" Poppy demanded to know.

"Not yet," I told her, "but I did write a book about accidentally killing a hummingbird called *Do You Love Me? Harry and the Terrible Whatzit* is about my fear of cellars. My admiration for people who are not afraid to be different was the idea behind *King Wacky*.

Gackenbach

Gackenbach

GACKENBACH

Hurray for Hattie Rabbit!

The Dog and the Deep Dark Woods

HARRY AND THE TERRIBLE WHATZIT

Harper & Row

SEABURY

129

"Sometimes an idea will come from an old tale. The idea for *Harvey, the Foolish Pig* came to me from an old Armenian tale. It is a tale of how we miss some of the great treasures in life because we fail to see them right smack under our nose. I really loved doing the pictures for that story."

"I am not surprised," said Poppy. "After all, you were an illustrator long before you were a writer."

"That's true," I said. "I worked as a graphic designer for twenty years in New York City before I moved to the countryside of Connecticut in search of a second career. I was forty-five years old, and I wanted to illustrate children's books—the works of other authors. I made the rounds of the publishing houses, but there were no books already written for me to illustrate. So what could I do? I sat down and wrote my own book, *Claude the Dog*. It was published, complete with my pictures, and so were sixty more books after that. It was a simple need for words that made an author out of me."

"Maybe if you had stayed in New York," Poppy mentioned, "we might be on Easy Street today, and I would be eating steak instead of dry dog food."

"Maybe," I replied, "but I would not be happy. I love what I am doing. I would rather write and illustrate children's books than anything else in the world."

"I just might like to become a writer, too," said Poppy, her eyes ablaze with imagination. "Do you have advice for me?"

"I should say so," I answered quickly. "Read," I said. "And keep a notebook! Write down all the things that happen to you. Write down what you feel and what you think. It will come in handy when you are ready to write."

I wondered as I rubbed Poppy's fat belly if this little beast might someday make good her threat to become a writer and put me to shame.

No! It's impossible! How could she ever learn to type?

Dick Gackenbach

There Was a Sad Pig with a Tail

by Arnold Lobel

There was a sad pig with a tail

Not curly, but straight as a nail.

So he ate simply oodles

Of pretzels and noodles,

Which put a fine twist to his tail.

Pulling the Theme Together

1. Welcome to Woosey! Do you like living in King Wacky's backward kingdom? Explain your reasons.

2. We learn from the twists and turns in our lives. Think about Chicken Little, Anansi, Harvey, and the kids in Miss Nelson's class. If you were talking with them, what would they say they learned?

3. Think about a game that you like to play. Now imagine playing it with some of the characters in this book. How might your game be different when you play with some of these characters?

Books
to Enjoy

Wild Willie and
King Kyle, Detectives
by Barbara M. Joosse
Clarion, 1993
Life is perfect for best
friends Willie and Kyle, until
Kyle moves away and a girl
moves in next door. Willie
wonders if life will ever be
the same.

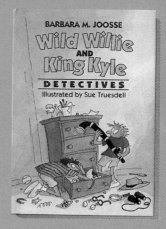

Too Many Tamales
by Gary Soto
Putnam, 1993
When Maria loses her
mother's diamond ring in
a batch of tamale dough,
she can think of only one
way to find it.

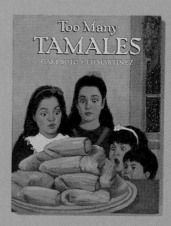

Nanny Goat and the Seven Little Kids

Retold by Eric A. Kimmel
Illustrations by Janet Stevens
Holiday House, 1992

The forests in folk tales are full of big, bad wolves! When Nanny Goat must go to market and leave her seven kids home alone, the local wolf is soon at the door. Who will be more clever? Nanny Goat and her kids or the Big Bad Wolf?

Mystery on the Docks

Written and illustrated by Thacher Hurd
HarperCollins, 1984

Ralph is an opera-loving cook at the diner on Pier 46. When his favorite opera star is kidnapped by a gang of thugs, Ralph must use his wits to rescue his hero.

Donna O'Neeshuck Was Chased by Some Cows

by Bill Grossman
Illustrations by Sue Truesdell
HarperCollins, 1984

A simple pat on the head leads to a wild chase through farm and field. Why are all these cows and half the town running after little Donna O'Neeshuck?

Literary Terms

Animal Fantasy

A fantasy is a story that could not really happen. **Animal fantasies** are stories that have animal characters acting like people. Think about Harvey or Chicken Little. How do they act like real people?

Character

Characters are the people and animals in a story. Two characters in the same story can be very different. The author can show what characters are like by the way they talk. Miss Nelson talks in a sweet voice. Viola Swamp talks in an unpleasant voice. Which one do you like better?

Plot

Before writing a story, an author will plan a **plot**, a series of events that will happen during the story. Some stories have a surprise twist at the end. Were you surprised when King Wacky said, "We are at peace!" and his people believed him? Did you think Harvey would find his riches? Were you surprised at the ending?

Glossary

How to Use the Pronunciation Key

After each entry word in this glossary, there is a special spelling, called the **pronunciation.** It shows how to say the word. The word is broken into syllables and then spelled with letters and signs. You can look up these letters and signs in the **pronunciation key** to see what sounds they stand for.

This dark mark (ˈ) is called the **primary accent.** It follows the syllable you say with the most force. This lighter mark (ˈ) is the **secondary accent.** Say the syllable it follows with medium force. Syllables without marks are said with least force.

Full Pronunciation Key

a	hat, cap	**i**	it, pin	**p**	paper, cup	**ə**	stands for:
ā	age, face	**ī**	ice, five	**r**	run, try		a in about
ä	father, far			**s**	say, yes		e in taken
		j	jam, enjoy	**sh**	she, rush		i in pencil
b	bad, rob	**k**	kind, seek	**t**	tell, it		o in lemon
ch	child, much	**l**	land, coal	**th**	thin, both		u in circus
d	did, red	**m**	me, am	**ᴛʜ**	then, smooth		
		n	no, in				
e	let, best	**ng**	long, bring	**u**	cup, butter		
ē	equal, be			**u̇**	full, put		
ėr	her, learn	**o**	hot, rock	**ü**	rule, move		
		ō	open, go				
f	fat, if	**ô**	order, all	**v**	very, save		
g	go, bag	**oi**	oil, toy	**w**	will, woman		
h	he, how	**ou**	house, out	**y**	young, yet		
				z	zoo, breeze		
				zh	measure, seizure		

Words from your stories

a·corn (ā′kôrn), the nut of an oak tree. *noun.*

ar·rest (ə rest′), **1** to take to jail or court by authority of the law: *The police arrested the burglar.* **2** a stopping; seizing: *We saw the arrest of the burglar.* **3** to stop; check: *Filling a tooth arrests decay.* **1,3** *verb,* **2** *noun.*

a·void (ə void′), to keep away from; keep out of the way of: *We avoided driving through large cities on our trip. verb.*

back·fire (bak′fīr′), **1** an explosion of gas occurring at the wrong time or in the wrong place in a gasoline engine. **2** to explode unexpectedly in a car's engine: *The old car backfired, and we all jumped.* **3** to have a result opposite to the expected result: *His plan backfired, and instead of getting rich he lost his money.* **1** *noun,* **2,3** *verb,* **back·fires, back·fired, back·fir·ing.**

back·ward (bak′wərd), **1** with the back first: *He tumbled over backward.* **2** toward the back: *I looked backward.* **3** opposite to the usual way: *You have your jacket on backward. adverb.*

con·fuse (kən fyüz′), **1** to throw into disorder; mix up: *So many people talking at once confused me.* **2** to be unable to tell apart; mistake one thing or person for another: *People often confuse this girl with her twin sister. verb,* **con·fus·es, con·fused, con·fus·ing.**

con·sid·er (kən sid′ər), to think about in order to decide: *Before you suggest an answer, take time to consider the problem. verb.*

cos·tume (kos′tüm *or* kos′tyüm), **1** a way of dressing, including the way the hair is worn: *The kimono is part of the national costume of Japan.* **2** clothing worn on the stage, or for fun: *Jean wore a sailor costume to the party. The actors wore colonial costumes. noun.*

costume (def. 1)

a hat	i it	oi oil	ch child	ə stands for:
ā age	ī ice	ou out	ng long	a in about
ä far	o hot	u cup	sh she	e in taken
e let	ō open	ù put	th thin	i in pencil
ē equal	ô order	ü rule	ᴛн then	o in lemon
ėr term			zh measure	u in circus

de·serve (di zėrv′), to have a right to; have a claim to; be worthy of: *A hard worker deserves good pay. Reckless drivers deserve to have their licenses taken away.* verb, **de·serves, de·served, de·serv·ing.**

dis·cour·age (dis kėr′ij), **1** to take away the courage of; destroy the hopes of: *Failing again and again discourages anyone.* **2** to try to prevent by disapproving: *All her friends discouraged her from such a dangerous swim.* **3** to prevent or hinder: *The chill of coming winter soon discouraged our picnics.* verb, **dis·cour·ag·es, dis·cour·aged, dis·cour·ag·ing.**

e·mer·gen·cy (i mėr′jən sē), **1** a sudden need for immediate action: *I keep a box of tools in my car for use in an emergency.* **2** for a time of sudden need: *The surgeon performed an emergency operation.* **1** noun, plural **e·mer·gen·cies;** **2** adjective.

es·cape (e skāp′), **1** to get free; get out and away: *The bird escaped from its cage.* **2** to keep free or safe from: *We all escaped the measles.* **3** the act of escaping: *Their escape was aided by the thick fog.* **4** a way of escaping: *There was no escape from the trap.* **5** to fail to be noticed or remembered by: *I knew his face, but the name escaped me.* **1,2,5** verb, **es·capes, es·caped, es·cap·ing;** **3,4** noun.

fo·rest (fôr′ist), **1** thick woods; woodland, often covering many miles: *Many people work to save the rain forest from being cut down.* **2** of the forest: *Help prevent forest fires.* **1** noun, **2** adjective.

forest
The trees in the **forest** shaded the ground.

for·give (fər giv′), to pardon; excuse; give up the wish to punish: *Please forgive me for breaking your tennis racket. She forgave my mistake.* verb, **for·gives, for·gave, for·giv·en, for·giv·ing.**

for·giv·en (fər giv′ən), See **forgive.** *Your mistakes are forgiven, but be more careful.* verb.

hiss (his), **1** to make a sound like *ss,* or like a drop of water on a hot stove: *Geese and snakes hiss.* **2** a sound like *ss: Hisses were heard from many who disliked what the speaker was saying.* **3** to show disapproval of by hissing: *The audience hissed the dull play.* 1,3 verb, 2 noun, plural **hiss·es.**

ill-treat (il′trēt′), to treat cruelly; treat badly; do harm to; abuse: *The horses were rescued from the man who ill-treated them.* verb.

in·no·cent (in′ə sənt), **1** doing no wrong or evil; free from sin or wrong; not guilty: *In the United States a person is innocent until proved guilty.* **2** having a simple and trusting nature: *It was innocent of you to lend your bicycle to a stranger.* **3** doing no harm: *innocent amusements.* adjective.

in·ter·est·ing (in′tər ə sting), arousing interest; holding one's attention: *Stories about travel and adventure are interesting to most people.* adjective.

jour·ney (jėr′nē), **1** a traveling from one place to another; trip: *The Evans family took a journey around the world.* **2** to travel; take a trip: *She journeyed to Europe last summer.* 1 noun, plural **jour·neys;** 2 verb.

la·zy (lā′zē), **1** not willing to work or be active: *He lost his job because he was lazy.* **2** moving slowly; not very active: *A lazy stream winds through the meadows.* adjective, **la·zi·er, la·zi·est.**

leash (lēsh), **1** a strap or chain for holding an animal in check: *He led the dog on a leash.* **2** to hold in; control: *She leashed her anger and did not say a harsh word.* 1 noun, plural **leash·es;** 2 verb.

leash (def. 1)
The children kept the dog on a **leash.**

140

a hat	i it	oi oil	ch child	ə stands for:
ā age	ī ice	ou out	ng long	a in about
ä far	o hot	u cup	sh she	e in taken
e let	ō open	ú put	th thin	i in pencil
ē equal	ô order	ü rule	ŦH then	o in lemon
ėr term			zh measure	u in circus

mar·riage (mar′ij), **1** a living together as husband and wife; married life: *We wished the bride and groom a happy marriage.* **2** the ceremony of being married; wedding: *The townspeople attended the marriage of their princess to the king. noun.*

mis·chie·vous (mis′chə vəs), **1** full of mischief; naughty: *The mischievous child poured honey all over the kitchen.* **2** full of playful tricks and teasing fun: *My friends were feeling mischievous and hid my glasses as a joke. adjective.*

nuz·zle (nuz′əl), to rub with the nose; press the nose against: *My dog nuzzled my hand to tell me she was hungry. verb,* **nuz·zles, nuz·zled, nuz·zling.**

nuzzle
His horse **nuzzled** him.

peace (pēs), **1** freedom from quarreling or disagreement; condition of quiet, order, and security: *It is nice to have peace in one's home.* **2** freedom from war: *He works for world peace. noun.*

pop·u·lar (pop′yə lər), **1** liked by most people: *"Sky Fire" was voted the most popular rock song of the year.* **2** widespread among many people; common: *It is a popular belief that black cats bring bad luck. adjective.*

poul·try (pōl′trē), birds, such as chickens, turkeys, geese, or ducks, raised for their meat or eggs. *noun.*

prom·ise (prom′is), **1** words said or written, binding a person to do or not to do something: *You can count on her to keep her promise.* **2** to give one's word; make a promise: *They promised to stay till we came.* **3** an indication of what may be expected: *The clouds give promise of rain.* **1,3** *noun,* **2** *verb,* **prom·is·es, prom·ised, prom·is·ing.**

pro·pel·ler (prə pel′ər), a revolving part with blades, for propelling boats and aircraft. *noun.*

ques·tion (kwes′chən), **1** a thing asked in order to find out: *The teacher answered the children's questions about the story.* **2** to ask in order to find out: *Then the teacher questioned the children about what happened in the story.* **3** a matter of doubt or dispute: *A question arose about who owned the football.* **1,3** *noun,* **2** *verb.*

141

rich (rich), **1** having much money, land, goods, or other property: *That movie star is a rich man.* **2** well supplied: *a country rich in oil. adjective.*

rush (rush), **1** to move with speed or force: *The river rushed past.* **2** to send, push, or force with speed or haste: *Rush this order, please.* **3** to go or act with great haste: *They rush into things without knowing anything about them. verb.*

se·cret (sē′krit), **1** kept from the knowledge of others: *a secret errand, a secret weapon.* **2** something secret or hidden: *Can you keep a secret?* **3** hidden: *a secret drawer.* **4** working or acting in secret: *the secret police, a secret agent.* **1,3,4** *adjective,* **2** *noun.* **in secret,** secretly; privately; not openly: *I have said nothing in secret that I would not say openly.*

sense·less (sens′lis), **1** unconscious: *A hard blow on the head knocked him senseless.* **2** foolish; stupid: *a senseless idea. adjective.*

shy (shī), **1** uncomfortable in company; bashful: *He is shy and dislikes parties.* **2** easily frightened away; timid: *A deer is a shy animal. adjective,* **shy·er, shy·est,** or **shi·er, shi·est.**

squirm (skwėrm), to wriggle; writhe; twist: *The restless girl squirmed in her seat. verb.*

steal (stēl), **1** to take something that does not belong to one; take dishonestly: *If you leave your bike unlocked, someone may steal it.* **2** to take, get, or do secretly: *She stole time from her lessons to read a story.* **3** (in baseball) to run to second base, third base, or home plate as the pitcher throws the ball to the catcher. *verb,* **steals, stole, sto·len, steal·ing.**

secret (def, 2)
What **secret** are they sharing?

a hat	i it	oi oil	ch child	ə stands for:
ā age	ī ice	ou out	ng long	a in about
ä far	o hot	u cup	sh she	e in taken
e let	ō open	ú put	th thin	i in pencil
ē equal	ô order	ü rule	ŦH then	o in lemon
ėr term			zh measure	u in circus

sto·len (stō′lən), See **steal**. *The money was stolen by a thief.* verb.

strange (strānj), **1** unusual; odd; peculiar: *A strange quiet fell over the town just before the storm.* **2** not known, seen, or heard of before; not familiar: *She is moving to a strange place. A strange cat is on our steps.* **3** out of place; not at home: *The poor child felt strange in the palace.* adjective, **strang·er, strang·est.**

tri·al (trī′əl), **1** the examining and deciding of a case in court: *The suspect was brought to trial.* **2** the process of trying or testing: *The mechanic gave the motor another trial to see if it would start.* **3** trouble: hardship: *The pioneers suffered many trials.* noun.
on trial, 1 being tried or tested: *He is employed for two weeks on trial.* **2** being tried in a court of law: *The suspect goes on trial next Monday.*

trou·sers (trou′zərz), a two-legged outer article of clothing reaching from the waist to the ankles; pants: *He ripped his trousers climbing over the fence.* noun plural.

un·pleas·ant (un plez′nt), not pleasant; disagreeable: *The broken machine had an unpleasant sound.* adjective.

un·u·su·al (un yü′zhü əl), not in common use; not common; rare; beyond the ordinary: *We had trouble believing his unusual story.* adjective.

wed·ding (wed′ing), **1** a marriage ceremony: *I carried the rings on a pillow at my aunt's wedding to Mr. Parker.* **2** an anniversary of it. *A golden wedding is the fiftieth anniversary of a marriage.* noun.

wick·ed (wik′id), **1** bad; evil; sinful: *The wicked king threw many people into prison.* **2** mischievous; playfully sly: *a wicked smile.* **3** unpleasant; severe: *A wicked snowstorm swept through the state.* adjective.

unusual
an **unusual** hairstyle

143

Acknowledgments

Text
Pages 6–22: *Miss Nelson Is Missing* by Harry Allard, illustrated by James Marshall. Copyright © 1977 by Harry Allard. Illustrations © 1977 by James Marshall. Reprinted by permission of Houghton Mifflin Company.

Pages 24–44: *Esmeralda and the Pet Parade* by Cecile Schoberle. Copyright © 1990 by Cecile Schoberle. Reprinted with the permission of Simon & Schuster Books for Young Readers.

Pages 46–47: "A Goat Wandered into a Junkyard" from *Something Big Has Been Here* by Jack Prelutsky, illustrations by James Stevenson. Copyright © 1990 by Jack Prelutsky. Illustrations copyright © 1990 by James Stevenson. Reprinted by permission of Greenwillow Books, a division of William Morrow & Company, Inc.

Pages 48–68: *Anansi and the Moss-Covered Rock* retold by Eric A. Kimmel, illustrated by Janet Stevens. Text copyright © 1988 by Eric A. Kimmel. Illustrations copyright © 1988 by Janet Stevens. Reprinted by permission of Holiday House. All rights reserved.

Pages 70–90: Text and illustrations from *Chicken Little*, retold and illustrated by Steven Kellogg. Copyright © 1985 by Steven Kellogg. Reprinted by permission of Morrow Junior Books, a division of William Morrow & Company, Inc.

Pages 92–110: *Harvey, the Foolish Pig* by Dick Gackenbach. Text and illustrations copyright © 1988 by Dick Gackenbach. Reprinted by permission of Clarion Books, a Houghton Mifflin Company imprint.

Pages 112–127: *King Wacky* by Dick Gackenbach. Copyright © 1984 by Dick Gackenbach. Reprinted by permission of McIntosh and Otis, Inc.

Pages 128–131: "Conversations with My Dog" by Dick Gackenbach. Copyright © 1991 by Dick Gackenbach.

Page 132: "There Was a Sad Pig with a Tail" from *The Book of Pigericks: Pig Limericks* by Arnold Lobel. Copyright © 1983 by Arnold Lobel. Reprinted by permission of HarperCollins Publishers.

Artists
Illustrations owned and copyrighted by the illustrator.
Henrik Drescher, cover, 1–5, 134–135
James Marshall, 6–23
Cecile Schoberle, 24–45
James Stevenson, 46–47
Janet Stevens, 48–69
Steven Kellogg, 70–91
Dick Gackenbach, 92–131
Arnold Lobel, 132

Photographs
Unless otherwise acknowledged, all photographs are the property of Scott Foresman.
Page 128 (right): Courtesy of Dick Gackenbach
Page 139: Don and Pat Valenti
Page 140: Tim Davis/Photo Researchers
Page 143: Buck Campbell/FPG

Glossary
The contents of the Glossary have been adapted from *Beginning Dictionary*, Copyright © 1988, Scott, Foresman and Company.